YEAR 3

Classwo

Fiction and Poetry Texts

Eileen Jones

Published in 2004 by:
Nelson Thornes Ltd
Delta Place
27 Bath Road
CHELTENHAM
GL53 7TH
United Kingdom

04 05 06 07 08 / 10 9 8 7 6 5 4 3 2 1

A catalogue record for this book is available from the British Library

ISBN 0-7487-8647-3

Illustrations by Martha Hardy, Mike Phillips, Nick Schon and Lisa Williams
Page make-up by GreenGate Publishing Services

Printed in Great Britain by Ashford Colour Press

Acknowledgements
All texts written by and copyright Eileen Jones except:

Barmkins are Best by Joan Aiken from *Moon Cake and Other Stories* reproduced by permission of Hodder and Stoughton Limited; *Harry Potter and the Philosopher's Stone* Copyright © J K Rowling 1997; Extract from *Pippi Longstocking* by Astrid Lindgren translated by Edna Hurup (OUP, 1954), Copyright © Saltkraken AB/Astrid Lindgren, reprinted by permission of Oxford University Press; *Fantastic Mr Fox* Copyright © Roald Dahl published by Unwin Hyman Ltd pp79–81; *Fantastic Mr Fox – A Play* Copyright © Roald Dahl and Sally Reid published by Puffin books pp52–59; 'City Lights' from *Your Turn Next*. Text Copyright © Margaret Greaves 1966. Published by Egmont Books Limited, London and used with permission; 'Wonderbirds' by Patricia Leighton taken from *The Works 2* by permission of Macmillan Publishers Ltd (2000) Copyright © Patricia Leighton; 'Anancy and Common Sense' by Louise Bennett from *The Tinderbox Assembly Book* published by A&C Black Publishers Ltd Copyright © 1982; *The Crocodile's Blessing* original edition first published in 2000 in *The Fabrics of Fairytale* published by Barefoot Books Ltd, Bath UK. Text Copyright © 2000 by Tanya Robyn Batt; 'One Pink Sari' by Ann Marie Linden Copyright © Ann Marie Linden; 'Mother Parrot's Advice to her Children' (Ganda, Africa) translated by A K Nyabongo taken from *Because a Fire Was in My Head: 101 Poems to Remember* edited by Michael Morpurgo. Reproduced by permission of Faber and Faber Ltd, 3 Queen Square, London, WC1N 3AU; 'Friendship' by Véronique Tadjo taken from *Talking Drums* published by A&C Black Publishers Ltd Copyright © Véronique Tadjo; 'King Canute' Copyright © Paul Bright 2002, first published in *The Works 2* (Macmillan Publishers Ltd); 'The Holiday' taken from *The Fib and Other Stories* by George Layton reproduced by permission of Macmillan Children's Books, London UK. Copyright © George Layton 1978; From *The Marble Crusher*. Text Copyright © Michael Morpurgo 1992. Published by Egmont Books, Limited, London and used with permission; From *Bill's New Frock*. Text Copyright © Anne Fine 1989. Published by Egmont Books Limited, London and used with permission; 'Jim who ran away from his nurse, and was eaten by a lion' by Hilaire Belloc reprinted by permission of PFD on behalf of The Estate of Hilaire Belloc Copyright © 1970 by The Estate of Hilaire Belloc; *Mortimer's Cross* by Joan Aiken Copyright © 1982, 1983 by Joan Aiken Enterprises, Ltd. Reprinted by permission of Brandt & Hochman Literary Agents, Inc.; From *The Angel of Nitshill Road*. Text Copyright © Anne Fine 1992. Published by Egmont Books Limited, London and used with permission; From *Conker*. Text Copyright © Michael Morpurgo 1987. Published by Egmont Books Limited, London and used with permission.

Cover image: G81-230712 © Powerstock/age fotostock/Russ Bishop (rights managed)
Railroad steam train winding through fall aspens near Chama

Every effort has been made to trace the copyright holders but if any have been inadvertently overlooked, the publishers will be pleased to make the necessary arrangement at the first opportunity.

Contents

How to use this book

What this book contains	• Extracts from published works, plus tailor-made extracts, all arranged and chosen specifically to match the examples of medium-term planning provided by the National Literacy Strategy
	• Teaching ideas for each extract to get you started, covering some of the relevant text, sentence or word level objectives from the relevant unit

How you can use *Classworks Literacy Texts* with other resources	• The blocked unit structure means you can dip into the book to find resources perfect for what you're teaching this week – it doesn't matter what plan, scheme or other resource you're using
	• There are two *Classworks Literacy Texts* books for every year from Reception (or Primary 1) to Year 6 (or Primary 7): one contains Fiction and Poetry, the other contains Non-fiction. Both books together contain texts for every unit of the medium-term plans

What each page does

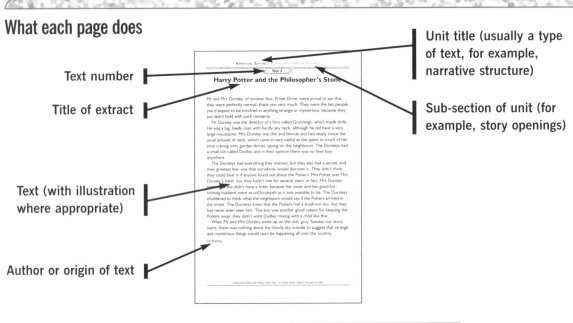

Text number
Title of extract
Text (with illustration where appropriate)
Author or origin of text

Unit title (usually a type of text, for example, narrative structure)
Sub-section of unit (for example, story openings)

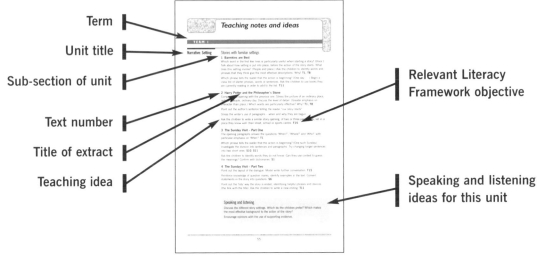

Term
Unit title
Sub-section of unit
Text number
Title of extract
Teaching idea

Relevant Literacy Framework objective
Speaking and listening ideas for this unit

Text 1

Barmkins are Best

Once there was a girl called Anna Freeway. She was not very big. Her father, Mr Freeway, was the owner of a huge chain of supermarkets. They were called Freeway Stores. Mr Freeway was very, very busy all week, running his stores. He worked in an office sixty storeys up. From its window you could see the sea, far away. But Mr Freeway never had time to look out of the window and see the sea.

Every Sunday, Mr Freeway took Anna for a walk. They always went Anna's favourite way – past the vet's surgery, where there were two big stone lions on each side of the door, past the war memorial where there was a big wreath of flowers, past the pond where there were swans and ducks, on to the common where there were gulls, and boys flying kites.

Mr Freeway never talked much. But Anna didn't mind. She liked looking about – at two pennies somebody had dropped on the path, at a sparrow that flew past carrying a bus ticket in its beak, at a man wheeling his rubber boots on a trolley. And she wondered about these things. Was the sparrow going to catch a bus, or had it just got off one? Who had dropped the pennies? Were the man's boots so tired that they had to be wheeled?

One day Mr Freeway was even quieter than usual.

Joan Aiken

Text 2

Harry Potter and the Philosopher's Stone

Mr and Mrs Dursley, of number four, Privet Drive, were proud to say that they were perfectly normal, thank you very much. They were the last people you'd expect to be involved in anything strange or mysterious, because they just didn't hold with such nonsense.

Mr Dursley was the director of a firm called Grunnings, which made drills. He was a big, beefy man with hardly any neck, although he did have a very large moustache. Mrs Dursley was thin and blonde and had nearly twice the usual amount of neck, which came in very useful as she spent so much of her time craning over garden fences, spying on the neighbours. The Dursleys had a small son called Dudley and in their opinion there was no finer boy anywhere.

The Dursleys had everything they wanted, but they also had a secret, and their greatest fear was that somebody would discover it. They didn't think they could bear it if anyone found out about the Potters. Mrs Potter was Mrs Dursley's sister, but they hadn't met for several years; in fact, Mrs Dursley pretended she didn't have a sister, because her sister and her good-for-nothing husband were as unDursleyish as it was possible to be. The Dursleys shuddered to think what the neighbours would say if the Potters arrived in the street. The Dursleys knew that the Potters had a small son too, but they had never even seen him. This boy was another good reason for keeping the Potters away; they didn't want Dudley mixing with a child like that.

When Mr and Mrs Dursley woke up on the dull, grey Tuesday our story starts, there was nothing about the cloudy sky outside to suggest that strange and mysterious things would soon be happening all over the country.

J K Rowling

Text 3

The Sunday Visit – Part One

It was February, 1888, and winter seemed never-ending. The ground had been covered with snow for over a month. The children were housebound, restricted to the nursery, playroom or schoolroom. The house was cold.

It was a large house, with the children's quarters on the third storey. These were small, confining rooms, largely unheated, for their father did not believe in mollycoddling. Their nanny's room, next to the nursery, was smaller still. She worked all day and was on call throughout the night. Permanently exhausted, she answered to the constant demands of four children and the imperious instructions of their parents. Her monthly visits home were her only, precious relief.

One such Sunday, while the baby slept and the rest of the family attended church, Dora dressed herself ready for the walk home. It would take one hour, but it would be worth it. Her mother would have a hot stew cooking, while her father cleared a new pathway through the snow. The younger children would be waiting with stories to tell of their doings, and the baby would be content to be petted. For Dora herself, there would be fussing and attention from her parents. Her mother would have packed a basket of home-baked cakes, ready for Dora to take back with her. Dora was warmed just by these thoughts.

Then the family returned from church…

Classworks Fiction and Poetry Texts Year 3 © Eileen Jones, Nelson Thornes Ltd 2004

The Sunday Visit – Part Two

Dora recognised this as her signal for departure. She hastened to put on her hat and coat, but a summons was made.

"Roberts, I wish to speak to you," came the voice.

Promptly, she went to the lower landing. The Master was standing waiting.

"Roberts, I have decided to cancel this month's visit. Further snowfall could impede your return. The Mistress must not risk being left without you. You will, therefore, wait until March's visit to make the journey to your village. Today, you will busy yourself assisting Cook in the kitchen. That will be all, Roberts."

With a bobbed curtsey, Dora fled to her room. How could she bear it? Her parents would be waiting for her. What would they think? She had no way to contact them. Wet-eyed, she replaced her uniform.

Sunday luncheon was a large, important meal. Cook set high standards and Dora was harped at, harried, and hustled as she performed kitchen tasks.

It was four-thirty before any staff were allowed to eat. They fed themselves from the family's leftovers, but there was a strict pecking order and Dora was near the bottom. At six o'clock, as she ate rejected, fatty pieces of cold mutton, she heard a familiar voice. Cook called sharply to her and she was instructed to go to the back door. Why? What had she done?

Her family, cold and weary, stood waiting outside with the precious basket. She had lost her visit home. However, in the end, the visit had come to her.

Classworks Fiction and Poetry Texts Year 3 © Eileen Jones, Nelson Thornes Ltd 2004

Text 5

Pippi Starts School

Having reached the age of nine, Pippi has decided to give school a try…

"If you'll first tell me your full name," said the teacher, "I shall enrol you in the school."

"My name is Pippilotta Provisionia Gaberdina Dandeliona Ephraimsdaughter Longstocking, daughter of Captain Ephraim Longstocking, formerly the terror of the seas, now Cannibal King. Pippi is really just my nickname, 'cause my father thought Pippilotta was too long to say."

"I see," said the teacher. "Well then, we shall call you Pippi too. But now perhaps we should test your knowledge a bit," she continued. "You're quite a big girl, so you probably know a great deal already. Let us begin with arithmetic. Now Pippi, can you tell me how much seven and five make?"

Pippi looked rather surprised and cross. Then she said, "Well, if *you* don't know, don't think I'm going to work it out for you!"

All the children stared in horror at Pippi. The teacher explained to her that she wasn't to answer that way at school. She wasn't to call the teacher just 'you' either; she was to call the teacher 'ma'am'.

"I'm awfully sorry," said Pippi apologetically. "I didn't know that. I won't do it again."

"No, I should hope not," said the teacher. "And now I'll tell you that seven and five make twelve."

"You see!" said Pippi. "You knew it all the time, so why did you ask, then? Oh, what a blockhead I am! Now I called you just 'you' again. 'Scuse me," she said, giving her ear a powerful pinch.

The teacher decided to pretend that nothing was the matter.

"Now, Pippi, how much do you think eight and four make?"

"I s'pose round about sixty-seven?" said Pippi.

"Not at all," said the teacher. "Eight and four make twelve."

"Now, now, my good woman, that's going too far," said Pippi. "You said yourself just now that it was seven and five that made twelve. There oughter be *some* order, even in school. If you're so keen on this silly stuff, why don't you sit by yourself in a corner and count, and let us be in peace so we can play tag? Oh, dear! Now I said just 'you' again," she said with horror. "Can you forgive me this last time too? I'll try to remember better from now on."

Astrid Ericsson Lindgren (translated by Edna Hurup)

Text 6

A Technical Problem

St Olaf's, the oldest school in the town, was famed for its high standards. The headmaster, Mr Richards, made everything run like clockwork. All his teachers were expected to keep perfect order, and his favourite sound was the scratching of pens on paper. He was particularly fussy about equipment.

Miss Bundle was his newest teacher. She was not doing very well. Today was even worse than usual. Everything was going wrong. Her class was being particularly difficult; she had lost her planning file, so was not sure what lesson came next; the bulb had broken in the overhead projector, so she was pointing at words that were invisible; and now the television would not work.

"Leave it to me, Miss Bundle," called out Max Allway, the class nuisance, as he raced across the room.

"Watch out!" screamed an agitated Miss Bundle.

Too late – Max was already spreadeagled on the floor. The school's television lay next to him.

"Now we'll miss our programme," wailed Jade.

"It's the last episode!" shrieked Jodie. "We'll never find out what happened."

"It's your fault, Max."

"She should've had the TV ready."

"My mum says she's not organised enough."

The noise increased as the children hurled complaints at one another and at Miss Bundle. At any moment the headmaster could appear. Then what? Most likely, she'd be forced to pay for a new television and even lose her job. If she could just get the class quiet, salvage the television from the floor, then – just maybe – she would be safe. What on earth would quieten them?

Then the answer came to her...

Classworks Fiction and Poetry Texts Year 3 © Eileen Jones, Nelson Thornes Ltd 2004

A Practical Solution

Yes… that was it! She would let them have a first reading of their Class Assembly play. Class Assemblies were important dates in Mr Richards's calendar, and this was to be Miss Bundle's first attempt. She had better get it right.

"**Listen**, everyone." Miss Bundle knew that she was screeching, but it was the only way that she could make herself heard. "**Play. Play**. We are going to start our play."

Gradually, noise subsided. Max was disentangled from the television cable; the television was hauled back onto its stand; children sat down; and they waited to hear what was to be said.

"I'm… er, er, going to give out parts for our Assembly play," Miss Bundle said nervously. (She did not want to start them off again.) "I'll… er… choose the **quietest** people."

The bribe worked. She explained that *News* was to be the theme of the play. They would present a week of school news, using the format of television reporting. Hurriedly, she handed out the pre-prepared scripts. Parts were allocated and the first reading began:

NARRATOR: This morning we are going to teach you a little about news.

CHORUS: News is all about us,
News is in the eye.
News is what a person does
News is how the ratings lie.

News is about the common man,
Or astronauts reaching Mars.
News is how a sprinter ran,
Or learning about the stars.

TELEVISION
PRESENTER 1: Good evening, and welcome to…

Miss Bundle breathed a sigh of relief, as the rest of the lesson passed smoothly. She had managed to get through another day.

Classworks Fiction and Poetry Texts Year 3 © Eileen Jones, Nelson Thornes Ltd 2004

Text 8

Fantastic Mr Fox

At that moment they heard a woman's voice calling out in the house above them. "Hurry up and get that cider, Mabel!" the voice called. "You know Mr Bean doesn't like to be kept waiting! Especially when he's been out all night in a tent!"

The animals froze. They stayed absolutely still, their ears pricked, their bodies tense. Then they heard the sound of a door being opened. The door was at the top of a flight of stone steps leading down from the house to the cellar.

And now someone was starting to come down those steps.

"I'll be glad when the rotten brute is killed and strung up on the front porch," she called out. "And by the way, Mrs Bean, your husband promised I could have the tail as a souvenir."

"The tail's been all shot to pieces," said the voice from upstairs. "Didn't you know that?"

"You mean it's *ruined*?"

"Of course it's ruined. They shot the tail but missed the fox."

"Oh heck!" said the big woman. "I did so want that tail!"

"You can have the head instead, Mabel. You can get it stuffed and hang it on your bedroom wall. Hurry up now with that cider!"

"Yes, Ma'am, I'm coming," said the big woman, and she took a second jar from the shelf.

If she takes one more, she'll see us, thought Mr Fox. He could feel the Smallest Fox's body pressed tightly against his own, quivering with excitement.

"Will two be enough, Mrs Bean, or shall I take three?"

"My goodness, Mabel, I don't care so long as you get a move on!"

"Then two it is," said the huge woman, speaking to herself now. "He drinks too much anyway."

Carrying a jar in each hand and with the rolling-pin tucked under one arm, she walked away across the cellar. At the foot of the steps she paused and looked around, sniffing the air. "There's rats down here again, Mrs Bean. I can smell 'em."

"Then poison them, woman, poison them! You know where the poison's kept."

"Yes, Ma'am," Mabel said. She climbed slowly out of sight up the steps. The door slammed.

"Quick!" said Mr Fox. "Grab a jar each and run for it!"

Rat stood on his high shelf and shrieked. "What did I tell you! You nearly got nabbed, didn't you? You nearly gave the game away! You keep out of here from now on! I don't want you around! This is my place!"

"*You,*" said Mr Fox, "are going to be poisoned."

"Poppycock!" said Rat. "I sit up here and watch her putting the stuff down. She'll never get *me.*"

Mr Fox and Badger and the Smallest Fox ran across the cellar clutching a gallon jar each. "Goodbye, Rat!" they called out as they disappeared through the hole in the wall. "Thanks for the lovely cider!"

"Thieves!" shrieked Rat. "Robbers! Bandits! Burglars!"

Roald Dahl

Classworks Fiction and Poetry Texts Year 3 © Eileen Jones, Nelson Thornes Ltd 2004

Text 9

Fantastic Mr Fox

MRS BEAN *[Off-stage]*: Hurry up and get that cider, Mabel! You know Mr Bean doesn't like to be kept waiting, especially when he's been out all night in the cold.

[Sound of a door opening and footsteps coming down to the cellar]

MR FOX: Quick! Hide!

[All three, plus RAT hide behind the row of large flagons. MABEL enters stage left and starts looking slowly and deliberately along the shelves of cider jars. She carries a rolling pin]

MABEL: *[Shouting to MRS BEAN]*: How many will he want this time, Mrs Bean?

MRS BEAN *[Off-stage]*: Bring up two or three jars.

MABEL: He drank four yesterday, Mrs Bean.

MRS BEAN *[Off-stage]*: Yes, but he won't want that many today because he's not going to be up there more than a few hours longer. He says the fox is bound to make a run for it, this morning. It can't possibly stay down that hole another day without food.

MABEL *[Removing jar from shelf close to MR FOX's head]*: I'll be glad when the rotten brute is killed and strung up on the front porch. And by the way, Mrs Bean, your husband promised I could have the tail as a souvenir.

MRS BEAN *[Off-stage]*: The tail's been all shot to pieces. Didn't you know that?

MABEL: You mean it's *ruined*?

MRS BEAN *[Off-stage]*: Of course it's ruined. They shot the tail but missed the fox.

MABEL: Oh heck! I did so want the tail!

MRS BEAN *[Off-stage]*: You can have the head instead, Mabel. You can get it stuffed and hang it on your bedroom wall. Hurry up now with that cider!

MABEL: Yes, ma'am, I'm coming.
[Removes a second jar off shelf. If next jar is taken, MR FOX's head will be seen] Will two be enough, Mrs Bean, or shall I take three?

MRS BEAN *[Off-stage]*: My goodness, Mabel, I don't care so long as you get a move on.

Text 10

Fantastic Mr Fox
(continued)

MABEL: Then two it is. *[To herself]* He drinks too much anyway. *[Jar in each hand, rolling pin tucked under one arm, she goes to door stage left, pauses and sniffs]* There's rats down here again, Mrs Bean, I can smell 'em.

MRS BEAN *[Off-stage]*: Then poison them, woman, poison them! You know where the poison's kept.

MABEL: Yes, Ma'am. *[Exits stage left. Her footsteps are heard climbing slowly upstairs. Door slams]*

MR FOX *[Coming out, with others from behind flagons]*: Quick! Grab a jar each and run for it!

RAT *[Shrieking and dancing about]*: What did I tell you! You nearly got nabbed, didn't you? You nearly gave the game away! You keep out of here from now on! I don't want you around! This is my place!

MR FOX: You… *[Poking him in the chest]*… are going to be poisoned.

RAT: Poppycock! I sit up here and *watch* her putting the stuff down. She'll never get *me*.

MR FOX, MR BADGER AND SMALL FOX 4 *[Climbing back through the hole in the wall, each clutching a jar]*: Goodbye, Rat. Thanks for the lovely cider!

RAT *[Jumping about in rage]*: Thieves! Robbers! Bandits! Burglars!

[Lights fade. Spotlight on MR FOX and SMALL FOX 4, on the other side of wall. MR FOX is putting "bricks" back]

MR FOX: I can still taste that glorious cider. What an impudent fellow rat is.

MR BADGER: He has bad manners. All rats have bad manners. I've never met a polite rat yet.

MR FOX: And he drinks too much. *[Putting last "brick" in place]* There we are. Now home to the feast.

End of Scene 7

Roald Dahl and Sally Reid

Text 11

Making News

NARRATOR [*Walks to middle of stage*]:

This morning we are going to teach you a little about news.

[*Leaves stage*]

CHORUS [*At back or side of stage*]:

News is all about us,
News is in the eye.
News is what a person does,
News is how the ratings lie.

News is about the common man,
Or astronauts reaching Mars.
News is how a sprinter ran,
Or learning about the stars.

TELEVISION PRESENTER 1 [*Seated at a desk; cameramen can be seen facing the presenter*]: Good evening, and welcome to Monday's news from St Olaf's. Today has been a very quiet day at the school, with Miss Bundle's class continuing to maintain the highest of standards.

PRODUCER [*Appears in front of camera*]:

Stop. I think we're going to need a change there. Scriptwriter! [*A flushed lady comes running onto stage, carrying clipboard and sheets of paper*] I want something about that TV chaos.

SCRIPTWRITER: It's er, er, very short notice, but I'll do my best.

DIRECTOR [*Standing at side of stage*]:

This is ridiculous. Move on to the weather.

WEATHER PRESENTER [*Walks on carrying a map*]: This is the likely weather picture for tomorrow. Pretty straightforward, what? It's rain here, rain there, and there, and there, and over here, and…

TELEVISION NEWS PRESENTER 2 [*Seated at desk*]: Oh for goodness' sake! Why do you always have to go on and on? It's just to make sure you stay on screen, isn't it?

Text 12

Fantastic Mr Fox

Scene Eight

BOGGIS, BUNCE and BEAN take up waiting positions at B, sitting on camp stools, slumped over guns on laps. Curtain opens. Huge table with animals around it. Everyone eating and talking. MRS FOX and MRS BADGER are going round filling up plates. Air of great festivity.

MRS FOX: Eat up, everybody! Thanks to my wonderful, marvellous husband, there's enough for two or even three helpings. You must all be so hungry!

MR MOLE: It was becoming a nightmare. Every time I popped my head above ground, I found myself staring down the barrel of a gun.

MRS MOLE: We were so worried for the children. It's so difficult to keep an eye on them all the time.

MR WEASEL: We had the same problem. Very tricky. Tried everything. Crafty little things. Always giving me the slip. *[To MRS WEASEL]* Didn't they dear? I'll have another chicken leg, while you're passing, Mrs Fox, if you don't mind.

MRS WEASEL: You're right. But we were all getting so hungry, that was the chief worry. And now we're sitting down in front of this wonderful feast! Your husband deserves a medal, Mrs Fox. Oh my, is that really smoked ham?

MRS RABBIT: You know it was so thoughtful of your husband, Mrs Fox, to send back those carrots and lettuces. I've never tasted fresher ones.

MRS BADGER *[Calls across table]*: How are you doing with that dish, Mrs Fox? Shall I bring in reinforcements?

MRS FOX: I think we're all right, dear.

MRS RABBIT *[Mouth full]*: This is wonderful, truly wonderful! We should have all got together before.

MRS MOLE: This duck is delicious! I really must have the recipe from you, Mrs Fox. And there's so much!

MRS FOX: Well, Mrs Badger shared the cooking and of course the children helped.

Roald Dahl and Sally Reid

Text 13

Fantastic Mr Fox (continued)

MRS WEASEL: If you young ones have had enough, you can get down.

SMALL WEASEL: Listen to this, Mum!

[At one table SMALL FOX 2 starts to sing]

Oh Boggis and Bunce and Bean,
One fat, one short, one lean,
Those horrible crooks,
So different in looks,
Were none the less equally mean.

[Laughter]

SMALL RABBIT: Badger's made up another verse. Shhh!

[SMALL BADGER climbs on table. Silence as he sings]

Oh Boggis and Bunce and Bean,
One fat, one short, one lean,
Faces crack when they smile,
You can smell 'em a mile,
We all scarper as soon as they're seen.

[Laughter]

MRS FOX: Shh, everybody, I can hear something from the tunnel.

[Assembly slowly settles. From outside the door they hear MR FOX singing in a rich tenor voice]

MR FOX: Home again swiftly I glide,
Back to my beautiful bride,
She'll not feel so rotten

As soon as she's gotten
Some cider inside her inside.

[Then]

MR BADGER: Oh poor Mrs Badger, he cried,
So hungry she very near died,
But she'll not feel so hollow
If only she'll swallow
Some cider inside her inside.

[MRS FOX and MRS BADGER visibly melt. MR FOX, MR BADGER and SMALL FOX 4 burst in]

MRS FOX: My darling! *[Hugging MR FOX]* We couldn't wait! Please forgive us.

[Everyone hugs MR FOX, MR BADGER and SMALL FOX 4. There is much hilarity and back-slapping. All sit down and continue eating. Shouts of "Pass Dad the duck", "More cider for Mr Badger", "Tell us all about it", etc. The three eat ravenously, then contentedly pause and lean back]

MR BADGER *[Stands, raising his mug]*: A toast! I want you all to stand and drink a toast to our dear friend who has saved our lives this day – Mr Fox!

ALL: To Mr Fox! *[All stand and raise glasses]* To Mr Fox! Long may he live!

Roald Dahl and Sally Reid

Classworks Fiction and Poetry Texts Year 3 © Eileen Jones, Nelson Thornes Ltd 2004

Text 14

November Night

Splashing   Spraying   Sizzling   Sprinkler

Spitting   Spotting

Spurting   Splitting

S   D   s

                                 E

p   R p   p

                                 U i   r

a   T p

                                 C i   i

r

k   N n   n

                                 U g   k

l   P   l

i   Top

                                 Taper   i

n   Hotter   n

                                 Hisses

g   Candle

                                 Roman   g

STEADY

READY

Text 15

City Lights

Huge round oranges of light
Ripen against the thin dark of the city sky,
Spilling their juice in warm pools
   on bare dry pavements.
Below them blink the traffic lights
   like the eyes of enormous cats
Crouching in the dark –
Crouching and breathing with the heavy purr of traffic;
And winking tail lights slide and dart
   like goldfish
In the pale streams pouring from
   shop windows.

Margaret Greaves

Text 16

The Mouse's Tale

'Fury said to
a mouse, That
he met in the
house, "Let
us both go
to law: *I*
will prose-
cute *you*. –
Come, I'll
take no de-
nial: We
must have
the trial;
For really
this morn-
ing I've
nothing
to do."
Said the
mouse to
the cur,
"Such a
trial, dear
sir, With
no jury
or judge,
would
be wast-
ing our
breath."
"I'll be
judge,
I'll be
jury,"
said
cun-
ning
old
Fury;
"I'll
try
the
whole
cause,
and
con-
demn
you to
death."'

Lewis Carroll

Classworks Fiction and Poetry Texts Year 3 © Eileen Jones, Nelson Thornes Ltd 2004

Text 17

Wonder Birds

In the forest's shadows
jewelled hummingbirds
wordsearch vibrant flowers;
up, down, across, diagonally,
backwards and forwards they fly.

Their tiny, rotor blade wings
make music on air.
they hover and sip,
hover and sip,
knitting patterns of words
across sheets of leaves:

```
                        s
                        w
                        i
                        f
        d e l i c a t e
        e
        f a n s
        t
          h
            g       m
              i   e
                r
              c   b
                u
    m   r
      i
    a   r
  l       a
            c
              l
                e
                  s
```

Patricia Leighton

Text 18

The Owl

When cats run home and light is come,
  And dew is cold upon the ground,
And the far-off stream is dumb,
  And the whirring sail goes round,
  And the whirring sail goes round;
    Alone and warming his five whits,
    The white owl in the belfry sits.

When merry milkmaids click the latch,
  And rarely smells the new-mown hay,
And the cock hath sung beneath the thatch
  Twice or thrice his roundelay,
  Twice or thrice his roundelay;
    Alone and warming his five whits,
    The white owl in the belfry sits.

Alfred Lord Tennyson

Text 19

A Pigeon and a Picture

One day, a pigeon flew near a picture. The picture was of a glass, and the glass had water in it. However, the impetuous pigeon, who never paused to look twice at anything, thought that he could see just cool, refreshing water in front of him.

Speedily and greedily, the pigeon threw himself at the water, ready to quench his thirst. Of course, the pigeon was flying at a picture. He smashed against the glass in the frame and broke his feathers. Stunned by the blow, the pigeon fell to the ground.

Enemies of the pigeon had been watching and waiting nearby. Now he was captured easily.

Moral

Very often, if people act hastily, they will regret it later.

Classworks Fiction and Poetry Texts Year 3 © Eileen Jones, Nelson Thornes Ltd 2004

Text 20

A Baboon and a Fox

The old king died, so the animals held a Council Meeting to decide on a successor. However, it was difficult to choose. There seemed to be a fault in each animal who wanted to be king. One was not handsome enough, yet another was too moody. One did not have the right height, while another lacked sufficient strength. Then stepped forward one animal who amused them all. It was a laughing, happy animal, with tricks and silly faces: the baboon. He would be king.

However, one animal was not pleased. The fox wanted the crown for himself. Slyly, he plotted to expose the baboon's foolishness. Whispering in his ear, the fox told him of buried treasure he had found.

"If you are to be king, the treasure should be yours," hissed the fox. "I will show you where it is."

The two animals went into the forest, where the fox pointed into a ditch: in the ditch was a box. As the baboon touched the box, the trap sprang. His fingers were caught! Gleefully, the fox raced to fetch the other animals.

"Do we want a king foolish enough to be caught by such a simple trick?" they questioned one another.

So the fox gained the crown.

Moral

A clever person can always outwit a popular fool.

Text 21

Osiris

Centuries past, the God who ruled Ancient Egypt also ruled the whole world. He was Atum-Re, but as he grew old, he looked for a successor. He chose Osiris, who was a wise, honourable man.

Osiris became a just and good ruler, who brought prosperity to his land and his people. However, Osiris had an enemy: Set, his own twin brother. Set, a wicked but cunning man, was jealous of his brother's success, and plotted to get rid of him.

He held a great feast, to which Osiris was invited. During the feast, Set produced an elaborately decorated chest.

"I will give this to anyone who lies in it and finds it a perfect fit," he proclaimed.

Every guest tried the chest out for size, but all failed the test – until Osiris had his turn. (Set had previously discovered all the King's measurements.) The fit was so tight that Osiris was trapped. The wicked Set closed the box, and threw it into the River Nile, leaving his brother drowned. His wife, Isis, was inconsolable.

However, Set did not have happiness for long. Isis brought up her son, Horus, and told him the story of his father's death. Once an adult, the good Horus never left the evil Set in peace, constantly waging war against him, as he battled for revenge.

As for Osiris, he became the powerful King of the Underworld, passing judgement on the souls of the dead as they sought entry to the world of the afterlife.

Text 22

The New Year Animals

Long, long ago, the gods told the animals that each of them was to have a year named after him. At first, the animals were delighted. Then they began to argue among themselves about the order of the years.

The debate went on and on, as each animal wanted to be first in the calendar. The more they discussed the question, the less they agreed. At last, the gods grew tired of the constant sound of their bickering. A solution was announced. The solution was to be a race.

The race was to be to swim from one bank of the river to the other. The first animal to reach the opposite bank would be the winner. He would name the leading year.

The race began as the animals dived into the water. Immediately, the stronger, quicker animals took the lead, while animals such as the boar trailed behind. However, there was one animal who was not strong, but he was very clever. He was the rat.

The rat knew about the ox's great strength, so – unnoticed – he leapt onto his back. As expected, the ox, with powerful swimming, led the way. However, just before the ox got to the bank on the other side, the rat jumped into the water, and then climbed onto dry land. The rat was declared the winner.

So it is that the Year of the Rat is the first year of the Chinese calendar.

Text 23

The Legend of King Canute

In times past, Canute was famed for his heroic deeds. His greatest enemy was Edmund Ironside, for both of them competed for the throne of England. After fierce battles, it was Canute who emerged victorious. He was crowned King of England.

Canute was not satisfied for long. Soon he was seeking the thrones of other countries. Already King of Denmark and England, he fought for a third country. Finally, he added the title of King of Norway to his list.

He now had a vast empire to defend and he held firm against many attacks. The attacks were frequent and dangerous, and it was only because of Canute's bravery and clever tactics that his empire remained safe. Some of his followers, however, thought that his success was because he could do anything. They flattered him constantly.

"Whatever you say can happen," said one.

"You have only to speak, and the world obeys," said another.

Canute was a wise man and he recognised such claims as ridiculous. He was determined to prove this to his flatterers. Having ordered that his throne be carried to the shore, Canute sat at the water's edge.

"Waves, I order you to stop," he commanded.

Nothing happened. The waves continued to break onto the beach and the water got nearer to his throne.

"Stop. Stop," he thundered.

The waves ignored him and crashed against his throne.

"No man can control nature," said the wise Canute.

Classworks Fiction and Poetry Texts Year 3 © Eileen Jones, Nelson Thornes Ltd 2004

Text 24

Anancy and Common Sense

Anancy is the trickster hero of Caribbean folk stories. Sometimes spider, sometimes man, he is guileful, treacherous and lazy, but also playful and even lovable. In this story his behaviour is at its worst:

Once upon a time, Anancy, feeling very greedy for power and wealth decided to collect all the common sense there was in the world. He thought that everyone would then have to come to him with their problems and he would charge dear for his advice. So, he set out to collect all the common sense in the world.

He collected and he collected, and all that he found he put in a large calabash. When he could find no more common sense, he sealed the calabash with a roll of dry leaves. Then, he decided to hide all the common sense, at the top of a very high tree, so that no one else could get at it.

Anancy tied a rope to the neck of the calabash, tied the two ends of the rope together and put the loop over his head, so that the calabash rested on his stomach.

He started to climb the tree, but found that the calabash was getting in his way. He tried again and again, but all in vain. Suddenly, he heard someone laughing behind him, and looked around to see a little boy.

"Stupid fellow," cried the little boy, "if you want to climb the tree, why don't you put the calabash behind you?"

Anancy was so annoyed to hear this little bit of common sense coming from a little boy, when he, Anancy, thought that he had collected it all, that he flung the calabash at the foot of the tree and broke it.

And so, common sense was scattered in little pieces, all over the world, and nearly everyone got a bit of it.

Anancy is the cause.

Traditional Caribbean tale, retold by Louise Bennett

Text 25

The Crocodile's Blessing
Story opening

Once there was a beautiful young girl called Damura, who lived with her father, stepmother and stepsister in a village by the edge of a great river. Everyone loved Damura. She always had a piece of fruit to share with the children who played on the streets, rice for the poor and a comforting word for the elderly. As she went about her work, she would sing happily and the birds and butterflies would hover above her in a halo of rainbow colours.

Damura's father was a fisherman whose work often took him far away. Then Damura's stepmother gave Damura the hardest work to do. But Damura never complained. As the years passed, Damura grew into a handsome young woman. Soon suitors would be lining up outside the home to ask the old fisherman for his daughter's hand in marriage.

One day Damura's stepmother called to her. "Damura, the head of the village is coming for a meal tomorrow. You are to take all the furnishings and our clothes down to the river and scrub them well," she ordered.

Damura had done all the household washing only two days ago, but she also knew it was pointless to argue with her stepmother. So she gathered together all she needed and walked down to the river.

But as she began washing her stepmother's finest sarong, the fast-flowing current snatched the cloth from her hands and swept it downstream. Damura gave a cry of despair. The river was deep and the current was strong, and the sarong quickly swept round a bend in the river. What was Damura to do? Heaving the basket of washing up higher on to the bank, she set off after the sarong, hoping that the river might sweep it up on to the bank further downstream. She walked for hours along the river bank until the sun sank low in the west. Then she sat down and began to weep.

"Damura, why are you weeping here by the river?" came a voice. "Is the sea not salty enough?"

Damura looked up. As she gazed out across the water, she noticed two large saucer-like eyes peering at her. They were the eyes of a crocodile.

Tanya Robyn Batt

The Crocodile's Blessing
Story ending

Damura and the handsome young man had a wonderful evening…

All evening the two of them talked, but at dawn, Damura stood up to leave.

"I have never known an evening to be so short or so interesting," exclaimed the son of the village head, taking Damura by the hand. "Please tell me your name and where you come from so that I may see you again."

Fearing her stepmother's anger, Damura shook her head and ran from the house, but in her hurry one of her golden sandals fell from her foot and lay in the dust. The son of the village head ran after Damura and stumbled upon the fallen sandal. He examined the beautifully-crafted shoe with sorrow. Would he ever see its owner again? Returning to his father's house, he declared that he would marry the woman who possessed the other sandal.

The village head sent his servants out into the village. At each house, they were greeted by eager women who tried desperately to convince the servants that the sandal was indeed theirs. But the sandal would fit no one and the other shoe was nowhere to be found.

Finally the servants knocked upon the door of the small house on the edge of the river. Damura answered but was quickly pushed aside by her stepmother and sister. Both tried the sandal but their feet were too coarse and large to fit it.

"What about the young woman in the corner?" asked the servant.

"What? Damura?" they snorted. "She didn't even go to the feast."

But the servant stretched out the sandal towards Damura, who took it and slipped it on her foot. Then she reached into the folds of her sarong and took out the other sandal. The stepmother and daughter looked on with a mixture of surprise and horror.

"I shall take you now to the house of the village head," smiled the servant.

Damura and the son of the village head were married at once, and they lived together in great contentment. As long as the river was their happiness, and as deep as the sea was their love.

Tanya Robyn Batt

Text 27

The Lead

At one time, there was a group of girls in school who were the best at everything. One of "The Gang" was sure to win the race, get the top mark, or shine in the Christmas show. This year's production was going to be *West Side Story*.

"Wow!" squealed Tracey. "I've seen the film twice, and it's fantastic."

"Maria – she's the leading girl," said Cassie. "That's the role to get."

"Right," agreed Meera, "so which of us has the brilliant singing voice?"

Beth preened herself. The part was obviously hers.

The next day, "The Gang" elbowed others aside in their rush to reach the music room.

"Why don't you have a go, Amy?" called out Beth, as she knocked one timid girl aside. Amy blushed as "The Gang" hooted with laughter.

During the audition, girl after girl sang her piece. Beth, louder than the rest put together, returned to class with smug certainty. When Miss Carr came into the room later, "The Gang" sat back and waited for the announcement.

"Did any girl not attend the audition?" asked Miss Carr.

A sole hand went up.

"Come along, Amy, and I'll try you now," said Miss Carr.

"The Gang" guffawed as Amy stood up. They were not laughing five minutes later.

"I am delighted to say that I have found Maria," announced Miss Carr. "I listened to some dreadful, screeching voices today, particularly the loudest ones. Amy's is wonderfully sweet and clear. She will play the lead."

The play was a wonderful success, and Amy became a star overnight. As for "The Gang", they were never quite the same again.

Classworks Fiction and Poetry Texts Year 3 © Eileen Jones, Nelson Thornes Ltd 2004

Text 28

One Pink Sari

One pink sari for a pretty girl,
Two dancing women all in a whirl,
Three charmed cobras rising from a basket,
Four fat rubies, in the Rajah's casket,
Five water carriers straight and tall,
Six wicked vultures sitting on the wall,
Seven fierce tigers hiding in the grass,
Eight elephants rolling in a warm mud bath,
Nine green parrots in the coconut tree,
Ten twinkling stars, a-twinkling at me!

Ann Marie Linden

Text 29

Mother Parrot's Advice to her Children

Never get up till the sun gets up,
Or the mists will give you a cold,
And a parrot whose lungs have once been touched
Will never live to be old.

Never eat plums that are not quite ripe,
For perhaps they will give you a pain;
And never dispute what the hornbill says,
Or you'll never dispute again.

Never despise the power of speech;
Learn every word as it comes,
For this is the pride of the parrot race,
That it speaks in a thousand tongues.

Never stay up when the sun goes down,
But sleep in your own home bed,
And if you've been good, as a parrot should,
You will dream that your tail is red.

Traditional story of the Ganda people of Uganda, translated by A K Nyabongo

Text 30

Friendship

Friendship
Is precious
Keep it
Protect it
You will need it
Don't throw it away
Don't break it
Don't neglect it
Keep it
Somewhere
In your heart
If you want to
Somewhere in your thoughts
If you want to
But keep it
For, friendship
Has no borders
And its boundary
Is that of the world
It is the colour
Of the rainbow
And it has the beauty
Of a dream
Never listen
To those who say
It doesn't exist any more
It is here
It is yours
When you want it
All you have to do is:
Open
Your eyes

Véronique Tadjo

Classworks Fiction and Poetry Texts Year 3 © Eileen Jones, Nelson Thornes Ltd 2004

King Canute

The noble King Canute, they said
Could waves and tide abash
Canute said, "All this flattery
Is really rather rash.
Let's make a little wager.
Do you have a little cash?"
Then he sat upon the beach, and waited. Splash! Splash!
  Splash!
Now the winds began to whistle
And the waves began to crash.
"Command it to recede," they said
"Do try it. Have a bash!"
Canute said sternly, "Turn! Begone!"
And twiddled his moustache
But all the time the waves kept coming. Splash! Splash!
  Splash!
"The tide is on the turn," they said
With confident panache.
"Just give it time. One minute more!"
Canute said, "Balderdash!
It's way above my ankles
And I think it's time to dash
'Cause I'm getting soaking wet with all this Splash! Splash!
  Splash!"

Paul Bright

Classworks Fiction and Poetry Texts Year 3 © Eileen Jones, Nelson Thornes Ltd 2004

Text 32

The Wind in a Frolic

The wind one morning sprung up from sleep,
Saying, "Now for a frolic! now for a leap!
Now for a mad-cap, galloping chase!
I'll make a commotion in every place!"
So it swept with a bustle right through a great town,
Creaking the signs, and scattering down
Shutters; and whisking, with merciless squalls,
Old women's bonnets and gingerbread stalls.
There never was heard a much lustier shout,
As the apples and oranges trundled about;
And the urchins, that stand with their thievish eyes
For ever on watch, ran off each with a prize.

Then away to the field it went blustering and humming,
And the cattle all wondered whatever was coming;
It plucked by their tails the grave, matronly cows,
And tossed the colts' manes all about their brows,
Till, offended at such a familiar salute,
They all turned their backs, and stood sullenly mute.
So on it went, capering and playing its pranks:
Whistling with reeds on the broad river's banks;
Puffing the birds as they sat on the spray,
Or the traveller grave on the king's highway.
It was not too nice to hustle the bags
Of the beggar, and flutter his dirty rags:
'Twas so bold, that it feared not to play its joke
With the doctor's wig, or the gentleman's cloak.
Through the forest it roared, and cried gaily, "Now,
You sturdy old oaks, I'll make you bow!"
And it made them bow without more ado,
Or it cracked their great branches through and through.

William Howitt

Classworks Fiction and Poetry Texts Year 3 © Eileen Jones, Nelson Thornes Ltd 2004

Text 33

The Wind in a Frolic
(continued)

Then it rushed like a monster on cottage and farm,
Striking their dwellers with sudden alarm;
And they ran out like bees in a midsummer swarm.
There were dames with their 'kerchiefs tied over their caps,
To see if their poultry were free from mishaps;
The turkeys they gobbled, the geese screamed aloud,
And the hens crept to roost in a terrified crowd;
There was rearing of ladders, and logs laying on
Where the thatch from the roof threatened soon to be gone.

But the wind had passed on, and had met in a lane,
With a schoolboy, who panted and struggled in vain;
For it tossed him, and twirled him, then passed, and he stood,
With his hat in a pool, and his shoe in the mud.

There was a poor man, hoary and old,
Cutting the heath on the open wold –
The strokes of his bill were faint and few,
Ere this frolicsome wind upon him blew;
But behind him, before him, about him it came,
And the breath seemed gone from his feeble frame;
So he sat him down with a muttering tone,
Saying, "Plague on the wind! was the like ever known?
But nowadays every wind that blows
Tells one how weak an old man grows!"

But away went the wind in its holiday glee;
And now it was far on the billowy sea,
And the lordly ships felt its staggering blow,
And the little boats darted to and fro,
But lo! it was night, and it sank to rest,
On the sea-bird's rock, in the gleaming west,
Laughing to think, in its fearful fun,
How little of mischief it had done.

William Howitt

No Peace for Tom
Chapter One: Just the Beginning

Tom wanted a quieter time this year. Last year's problems with a gang of bullies, the case of the punctured bike tyres, and the lethal computer virus, had been enough detective work. In Year Four there were more clubs open to him and there was definitely more homework. The last thing he needed was another mystery.

The mystery involved the new boy, Joe. He had been at the school one week and already just about everything that could go wrong had done. Tom suspected more than just bad luck.

"Someone thinks it's funny to hide your property," said Tom, as they both searched for Joe's missing sports kit. "We've got to keep our eyes skinned."

Nevertheless, problems continued. Joe's pencil case "emptied" itself; his homework was found in the bin; and books kept disappearing. Mrs Holden, his teacher, was losing patience. When his sketch book disappeared, her tone was icy.

"It's his own fault, Miss Evatt. He's always doing this! Just find him a piece of scrap paper." Miss Evatt, the student teacher, smiled at Joe sympathetically, but it did not change the result: his drawing looked inferior to the others.

At the end of the afternoon, it was no surprise when he failed to find his homework diary: he now expected disasters. As he and Tom collected their belongings from the cloakroom, Miss Evatt came to talk to him.

"Don't get downhearted, Joe; we're all absent-minded sometimes."

"That's the worry, Miss Evatt. It's nothing to do with Joe," explained Tom. You've only just started here, but things are being done to Joe. There are people in this class who don't want Joe to succeed at this school. Every effort he makes is sabotaged!"

As the boys walked across the playground, Tom made up his mind.

"We need to talk about this properly, and it must be tomorrow!"

No Peace for Tom
Chapter Two: Detectives at Work

"You're not going to give in to this blackmail!" declared Tom. "A bit of detective work is all that's needed. Right, pen and paper."

So they began. They listed all the strange incidents so far, and how they could have been avoided. Eventually, they had an action plan:

1. make constant checks on property
2. watch out for furtive behaviour
3. meet up at break times to record observations
4. seek adult help.

The next day, Tom appeared with an official-looking, spiral-bound note book, the agreed action plan on the first page.

"Let's try Point 4 now," said Joe. "I've just seen Miss Evatt start down the path."

Joe and Tom gave Miss Evatt details of "lost" items, such as bags and pencil cases; sinister happenings, such as eerie re-appearances and locked doors; and, of course, the events she had witnessed yesterday afternoon.

"I can help look after your things," she said, "and I can keep a check on what other people are doing."

At break time, the boys wrote up a progress report:

Thurs. 12pm
Giggling (Ellie and Jade)
Unnecessary trips past our table (Harry)
Suspicious loitering near Joe's locker (Alexander)
INCIDENTS: 0

No Peace for Tom
Chapter Three: Where does it lead?

Four weeks of constant detective work, and what was there to show? Suspicions, ideas, hunches, but never any real proof, even against a primary suspect. They badly needed some luck, and, on Thursday, it came.

The numeracy lesson had not gone well for Joe. His number generator had mysteriously unravelled itself and his ruler had disappeared. Miss Evatt had been quick to help, but Mrs Holden's patience was wearing thin. He was relieved to reach the end of the lesson.

"This homework may prove impossible, but don't panic! It is still division, but not as you've ever seen it. Your homework is to explain what you think the calculation means and how you could try to solve it. For once I shall not be unhappy if you cannot do this work, but I do expect ideas and notes."

Joe felt hopelessly confused. It was difficult to see why they were to attempt the impossible! He was just grateful that Tom would help. Joe glanced at Tom to see if he understood what Mrs Holden meant: he was surprised to see an uncharacteristically smug expression on his friend's face. A scheme was being hatched.

After school, Tom revealed his plan. The next step would need outside help and Tom knew just the right person.

Tom's father usually got home at about six o'clock, and Tom was waiting for him.

"Dad, do you understand any of this?" asked Tom, presenting him with Mrs Holden's worksheet. He looked at it, looked at Tom and then raised his eyebrows.

"Mmm, is this a test to see if I'm in the right job, Tom? I'm a maths professor. I have to be able to do more than long division! There's something else behind this request, isn't there?"

No Peace for Tom
Chapter Four: A Bit of Outside Help

It was time to give his father the whole story, including the ingenious plan. All that Dad needed to do was to complete the long division calculations, obviously correctly and write an explanation.

In less than two minutes, Tom had a completed piece of work, with an explanation on the back.

"I'm not quite sure your plan will work, but good luck," said his father.

"I'll do it!" declared Miss Evatt next morning, and so the plan moved into action.

She made a photocopy of Tom's homework, put the original in Tom's bag, and its copy in Joe's. (Joe's own homework sheet was in his pocket.) After that, she returned to the classroom and hoped.

"Everything's in place," whispered Miss Evatt, as she passed the boys' table. "Now we've just got to wait and see."

"I said the work was really too difficult," said Mrs Holden, after revealing the answers, "so nobody needs to feel embarrassed. Does anyone want to tell us how they got on?"

"I got full marks."

There was a gasp and everyone looked at Tom in awe and amazement. They knew he was clever, but this was…

"I got full marks as well," came a voice from the back of the room.

Classworks Fiction and Poetry Texts Year 3 © Eileen Jones, Nelson Thornes Ltd 2004

Text 38

No Peace for Tom
Chapter Five: Solved!

"The work was already done for you, wasn't it?" said Miss Evatt, turning to face Elliot.

Elliot nodded helplessly. Miss Evatt described how the trap was set. Tom joined in, recounting the full story of the campaign against Joe.

"Whoever took the photocopy did everything else," he concluded.

"My mother made me," came Elliot's mumbled words.

Elliot's surname was Miller and his mother worked at the school.

Events followed quickly one after another. A tearful Elliot was asked to explain himself. His mother had told him what to do. She'd given him the work just as he was coming in from play, and said he should say it was his. Then…

When Mrs Miller appeared, she tried to bluff her way out of the situation.

"Me? Touch a child's bag? How dare you! My Elliot is excellent with numbers! He did all that on his own."

"He said you gave it to him, Mrs Miller," Mrs Holden replied.

"I told you…" snapped Mrs Miller at her son.

"I want you to stop making me do things to Joe! I never wanted to hide his things," Elliot blurted out.

That was it – even Mrs Miller could see that Elliot had said too much. The headteacher was summoned, and the verdict was swift: Mrs Miller was dismissed.

After school, the boys said goodbye to Miss Evatt (it had been a dramatic final day for her), and thanked her. As for Tom, he made a silent wish:

No more mysteries – please!

The Holiday

It wasn't fair. Tony and Barry were going. In fact, nearly all of them in Class Three and Four were going, except me. It wasn't fair. Why wouldn't my mum let me go?

"I've told you. You're not going camping. You're far too young."

Huh! She said that last year.

"You said that last year!"

"You can go next year when you're a bit older."

She'd said that last year, too.

"You said that last year an' all."

"Do you want a clout?"

"Well you did, Mum, didn't you?"

"Go and wash your hands for tea."

"Aw, Mum, everybody else is going to school camp. Why can't I?"

Because you're coming to Bridlington with me and your Auntie Doreen like you do every year.

"Because you're coming to Bridlington with me and your Auntie Doreen like you do every year!"

I told you. Oh, every year the same thing; my mum, me, and my Auntie Doreen at Mrs Sharkey's boarding house. I suppose we'll have that room next door to the lavatory: a double bed for my mum and my Auntie Doreen, and me on a camp bed behind a screen.

"I suppose we'll have that rotten room again."

"Don't be cheeky! Mrs Sharkey saves that room for me every year – last week in July and first week in August. It's the best room in the house, facing the sea like that, and nice and handy for the toilets. You know how important that is for your Auntie Doreen."

George Layton

The Marble Crusher

The school had strict rules about marbles…

Even on the smooth floor in amongst the chair legs Albert went on winning. He was crouching under the teacher's table, taking careful aim, when Mr Manners came in behind him silently.

"Albert," he said. "Albert, are you playing marbles?"

"Oh… yes sir," and Albert remembered at once – he remembered the punishment too and he began to twiddle his hair.

"They will all have to go, all of them mind," said Mr Manners. "Empty your pockets, lad," and he held out a big chalky hand. "I'm surprised at you, Albert, and disappointed – very disappointed."

Albert took them out of his pocket one by one and dropped them into Mr Manners' hand. His winnings went first – the blood red too – and then last of all his six great heavy silver ball-bearings. It was as if his blood was being taken from him. The fist closed before his eyes and his marbles were gone.

"A pity, Albert," Mr Manners said, shaking his head. "A terrible pity. Lovely marbles too. But you were warned. And we cannot have people breaking school rules can we now?"

Michael Morpurgo

Classworks Fiction and Poetry Texts Year 3 © Eileen Jones, Nelson Thornes Ltd 2004

Text 41

Bill's New Frock

For Bill, now a girl, playtime was proving less enjoyable than usual…

"Get out of the way!"

"*We're* playing here!"

Bill picked himself up. He was astonished. Usually if anyone walked into the football game, the players just thought they'd decided to join in. "Come in on *our* side!" they'd yell. "Be our goalie! Take over!"

This time it was as if they weren't so much playing football around him as *through* him.

"Get off the pitch!"

"Stop getting in our way! Go *round*!"

It was the frock again! He knew it!

"I want the ball," yelled Bill to all the other players. "I just want to borrow it for a minute – for a bet!"

Games always stopped for bets. It was a rule. But they all acted as if they hadn't even heard him.

"Out of our *way*!"

"You're spoiling the *game*!"

The ball happened to bounce Bill's way again, so he leaped up and caught it in his hands.

"I *need* it," he explained. "Just for a moment."

The footballers gathered in a circle round him. They didn't look at all pleased at this interruption of the game. In fact, they looked rather menacing, all standing there with narrowed eyes, scowling. If this was the sort of reception the girls had come to expect, no wonder they didn't stray far from the railings. No wonder they didn't ask to play.

"Give the ball back," Rohan was really glowering now.

"Yes," Martin agreed. "Why can't you stay in your own bit of the playground?"

Mystified, Bill asked Martin:

"What bit?"

"The girls' bit of course."

Bill looked around. Girls were still perched along the nursery wall. Girls were still huddled in the porch. Girls still stood in tight little groups in each corner. No girl was more than a few feet into the playground itself. Even the pair who had been trying to mark out the hopscotch game had given up and gone away.

Anne Fine

Classworks Fiction and Poetry Texts Year 3 © Eileen Jones, Nelson Thornes Ltd 2004

Text 42

A Little Princess

It was Sara's first morning…

After Sara had sat in her seat in the schoolroom for a few minutes, being looked at by the pupils, Miss Minchin rapped in a dignified manner upon her desk.

"Young ladies," she said, "I wish to introduce you to your new companion." All the little girls rose in their places, and Sara rose also. "I shall expect you all to be very agreeable to Miss Crewe; she has just come to us from a great distance – in fact, from India. As soon as lessons are over you must make each other's acquaintance."

The pupils bowed ceremoniously, and Sara made a little courtesy, and then they sat down and looked at each other again.

"Sara," said Miss Minchin in her schoolroom manner, "come here to me."

She had taken a book from the desk and was turning over its leaves. Sara went to her politely.

"As your papa has engaged a French maid for you," she began, "I conclude that he wishes you to make a special study of the French language."

Sara felt a little awkward.

"I think he engaged her," she said, "because he – he thought I would like her, Miss Minchin."

"I am afraid," said Miss Minchin, with a slightly sour smile, "that you have been a very spoiled little girl and always imagine that things are done because you like them. My impression is that your papa wished you to learn French."

If Sara had been older or less punctilious about being quite polite to people, she could have explained herself in a very few words. But, as it was, she felt a flush rising on her cheeks. Miss Minchin was a very severe and imposing person, and she seemed so absolutely sure that Sara knew nothing whatever of French that she felt as if it would be almost rude to correct her. The truth was that Sara could not remember the time when she had not seemed to know French. Her father had often spoken it to her when she had been a baby. Her mother had been a Frenchwoman, and Captain Crewe had loved her language, so it happened that Sara had always heard and been familiar with it.

"I – I have never really learned French, but – but –" she began, trying shyly to make herself clear.

One of Miss Minchin's chief secret annoyances was that she did not speak French herself, and was desirous of concealing the irritating fact. She, therefore, had no intention of discussing the matter and laying herself open to innocent questioning by a new little pupil.

"That is enough," she said with polite tartness. "If you have not learned, you must begin at once. The French master, Monsieur Dufarge, will be here in a few minutes. Take this book and look at it until he arrives."

Sara's cheeks felt warm.

Frances Hodgson Burnett

Classworks Fiction and Poetry Texts Year 3 © Eileen Jones, Nelson Thornes Ltd 2004

Text 43

Jim who ran away from his nurse, and was eaten by a lion

There was a boy whose name was Jim;
His friends were very good to him.
They gave him tea, and cakes, and jam,
And slices of delicious ham,
And chocolate with pink inside,
And little tricycles to ride,
And read him stories through and through,
And even took him to the Zoo –
But there it was the dreadful fate
Befell him, which I now relate.

You know – at least you *ought* to know,
For I have often told you so –
That children never are allowed
To leave their nurses in a crowd;
Now this was Jim's especial foible,
He ran away when he was able,
And on this inauspicious day
He slipped his hand and ran away!
He hadn't gone a yard when – Bang!
With open jaws, a lion sprang,
And hungrily began to eat
The boy: beginning at his feet.

Classworks Fiction and Poetry Texts Year 3 © Eileen Jones, Nelson Thornes Ltd 2004

Text 44

Jim who ran away from his nurse, and was eaten by a lion (continued)

Now, just imagine how it feels
When first your toes and then your heels,
And then by gradual degrees,
Your shins and ankles, calves and knees,
Are slowly eaten, bit by bit.
No wonder Jim detested it!
No wonder that he shouted "Hi!"
The honest keeper heard his cry,
Though very fat he almost ran
To help the little gentleman.
"Ponto!" he ordered as he came
(For Ponto was the lion's name),
"Ponto!" he cried, with angry frown.
"Let go, Sir! Down, Sir! Put it down!"

The lion made a sudden stop,
He let the dainty morsel drop,
And slunk reluctant to his cage,
Snarling with disappointed rage.

But when he bent him over Jim,
The honest keeper's eyes were dim.
The lion having reached his head,
The miserable boy was dead!

When Nurse informed his parents, they
Were more concerned that I can say:–
His Mother, as she dried her eyes,
Said, "Well – it gives me no surprise,
He would not do as he was told!"
His Father, who was self-controlled,
Bade all the children round attend
To James's miserable end,
And always keep a-hold of Nurse
For fear of finding something worse.

Hilaire Belloc

Text 45

Bawling Bertie

Bouncing Bertie, what a joy!
Bonny, beefy, baby boy.
But bother, blow, piercing pain:
Bertie bleating yet again.
All day long – he squawked and squalled;
Through the night – he brayed and bawled.
Rapid rocking, to and fro.
Would it stop him? No! No! No!

Sounds got grimmer as he grew,
Local language turning blue.
Wailing, whining, on it went,
'Til there was a missive sent.
Nearest neighbours penned a note:
KID IS GETTING ON OUR GOAT!
His downcast dad let them in:
Council crew complete with bin.

So proud parents best beware:
Muffle those mites in your care.

Classworks Fiction and Poetry Texts Year 3 © Eileen Jones, Nelson Thornes Ltd 2004

From **The Dong with a Luminous Nose**

When awful darkness and silence reign
Over the great Gromboolian plain,
   Through the long, long, wintry nights;–
When the angry breakers roar
As they beat on the rocky shore;–
   When Storm-clouds brood on the towering heights
Of the Hills of the Chankly Bore:–

Then, through the vast and gloomy dark,
There moves what seems a fiery spark,
   A lonely spark with silvery rays
   Piercing the coal-black night,–
   A Meteor strange and bright:–
Hither and thither the vision strays,
   A single lurid light.

Slowly it wanders,– pauses,– creeps,–
Anon it sparkles,– flashes and leaps;
And ever as onward it gleaming goes
A light on the Bong-tree stem it throws.
And those who watch at that midnight hour
From Hall or Terrace, or lofty Tower,
Cry, as the wild light passes along,–
   "The Dong!– the Dong!
   The wandering Dong through the forest goes!
   The Dong! the Dong!
   The Dong with a luminous Nose!"

Edward Lear

Text 47

Mortimer's Cross

Aunt Olwen had come to stay, and she had brought her clock…

"Worth a mint, that clock is," said Aunt Olwen with satisfaction. Even she had heard the chimes.

"It's louder than Concorde," said the doctor. "You could get middle-ear disturbance listening to it. Better stick a sock in its stomach while you've got illness in the house. See you tomorrow, Mrs Jones."

Great-aunt Olwen followed Arabel and the doctor downstairs because she wanted some mothballs to tuck in between the bedclothes.

Down in the front hall, the first thing she saw was Mortimer. He had pulled the piano-stool across the dining-room, out into the hall, and up against the clock; he had hoisted the coal scuttle on top of the stool, and was now standing on the coal, with his eye pressed to the keyhole of the clock door.

"What in the world is *that*?" said Great-aunt Olwen sharply.

Her voice startled Mortimer. The coal scuttle was not very well balanced on the piano stool, and when Mortimer turned round, he and the scuttle fell off the stool, thumping heavily against the door of the clock, and strewing coal over the grey wall-to-wall carpet.

The clock began striking as if all the hours had been joined together between now and the year two thousand.

"Oh, mercy, mercy, what's happened, stop that awful noise!" wailed Mrs Jones from upstairs. "My head feels as if it's going to split in half like a coconut."

The doctor kicked the clock till it stopped striking, and then escaped from Number Six, Rainwater Crescent, shouting, "Get that prescription made up as soon as possible!"

Mortimer had fallen among the lumps of coal, and was just picking himself up. Disappointed in his plan for getting into the clock, he was now gazing very keenly at Great-aunt Olwen's hearing-aid.

"What's *that*?" said Great-aunt Olwen again. She had fetched a brush and pan, and was sweeping up the coal. She poked at Mortimer with the brush.

"That's Mortimer," said Arabel. "He's our raven."

"Raven, you call him? He looks to me like a black imp from the pit," said Aunt Olwen. "Into a bath he goes before I'm an hour older, or my name's not Olwen Gwladys Angharad Merlwyn Jones. Crawling with germs from head to toe, he is, without a shadow of doubt; no wonder Martha has flu, only surprising it isn't pleurisy, psittacosis, and Ponsonby's disease."

"Oh, please, I don't think Mortimer would like being bathed at all, he isn't used to that sort of thing," said Arabel.

"He'll be used to it soon," said Aunt Olwen ominously, making a grab for Mortimer.

In return he made a snatch for her hearing-aid.

Joan Aiken

Classworks Fiction and Poetry Texts Year 3 © Eileen Jones, Nelson Thornes Ltd 2004

Text 48

The Mystery of Mr Jones's Disappearing Taxi

Arabel and Mortimer were on a case...

"Well I never!" thought Arabel. "So *he's* the thief who takes all the books from the library! And he uses Pa's taxi to bring them here! If I can find where he puts the books, I'll tell Miss Acaster, and then she'll be so pleased that perhaps she'll let Mortimer into the library again."

Occupied by this interesting plan, Arabel picked up Mr Beeline's umbrella, which he had left lying by the empty trolley, hooked down the steps in her turn, and followed Mr Beeline. She had a strong suspicion, also, that Mortimer had somehow managed to get into the building, and she hoped that she might come across him.

And what *had* happened to Mortimer?

By the time Mr Beeline had driven away the taxi, Mortimer, curled up in the glove pouch was fast asleep. He woke up at the library, where Mr Beeline halted to pick up the books he had previously hidden in a concrete litter bin. Mortimer was so interested when a large load of books was put in the back that he wasted no time shouting "Nevermore" to scare the driver, but just quietly ate the first three volumes of Edward Gibbon's *Decline and Fall of the Roman Empire.* These lasted him as far as Rumbury Tower Heights. Mr Beeline never noticed Mortimer and he quietly slipped from the taxi while Mr Beeline was unloading his books, and walked over to the fountain.

For a long time, Mortimer had been wondering if it would be possible to sit on top of one of the fountain jets. The present time seemed a very good opportunity to try. While Mr Beeline was wheeling trolley-loads of books back and forth to the fire-escape, Mortimer clambered up the side of the stone tank which held the fountain, and waited until one of the end jets sank down as low as it would go. Then, as it started to rise again, Mortimer launched himself out with his wings – hop, flap – and landed exactly on top of the jet, which was so powerful that it did indeed begin to carry him up. Higher and higher went Mortimer.

"Kaaark!" he said joyfully. It was exactly like sitting on top of a rapidly growing palm tree. The fountain was rather cold underneath him, to be sure, but Mortimer did not mind that – his feathers were so thick and waterproof that the drops could not get through to his skin.

Joan Aiken

Text 49

The Angel of Nitshill Road

There was a new girl at the school…

Afterwards, no one could remember quite who it was who first guessed she was a real angel. There were enough clues, of course. Tracey overheard Mrs Brown complaining that Celeste had dropped "out of the blue". When Ian took the register to the school office he heard the secretary telling Miss Featherstone that the new girl had a "heavenly" accent. And Mr Fairway was reported to have muttered that Celeste was having "a bit of trouble coming down to earth".

Then Lisa remembered that Celeste's father hadn't walked off that first morning. Or driven. He'd *flown*!

And that reminded Penny. How had Celeste's granny got there in time to stop her being given the wrong name?

She'd *swooped*.

The little group who chummed down Nitshill Road had a chat at the corner.

"So what did Celeste's father want to call her, anyway?"

Penny pushed the sweet she was sucking into the pouch of her cheek, out of the way.

"Angelica, she told us."

"*Angelica!*"

Another clue!

Tracey raced back just as the bell was ringing for afternoon school. As they pushed and shoved their way back into the classroom, she whispered to everyone around her:

"Guess what Celeste means! I looked it up in our *Name Your Baby* book. Celeste means 'from heaven'."

They all peeped at Celeste. Just at that moment she was gazing up out of her fizzy halo of bright hair, and telling Mr Fairway:

"No, truly, I know this chair's old enough to have a beard, and wobbles frightfully. But it's as comfy as a cloud!"

Comfy as a *cloud*?

Anne Fine

Classworks Fiction and Poetry Texts Year 3 © Eileen Jones, Nelson Thornes Ltd 2004

Conker

Nick lived with Grandma and Old Station…

All his life Old Station had been like a big brother to Nick. Nick was nine years old now. He had watched Old Station grow old as he grew up. The old dog moved slowly these days, and when he got up in the morning to go outside you could see it was a real effort. He would spend most of the day asleep in his basket, dreaming his dreams.

Nick watched him that morning as he ate his cornflakes before he went off to school. It was the last day before half-term. Old Station was growling in his sleep as he often did and his whiskers were twitching.

"He's chasing cats in his dreams," said Grandma. "Hurry up, Nick, else you'll be late." She gave him his satchel and packed lunch, and Nick called out, "Goodbye," to Old Station and ran off down the road.

It was a windy autumn morning with the leaves falling all around him. Before he got to school he caught twenty-six of them in mid-air and that was more than he'd ever caught before. By the end of the day the leaves were piled high as his ankles in the gutters, and Nick scuffled through them on the way back home, thinking of all the bike rides he could go on now that half-term had begun.

Old Station wasn't there to meet him at the door as he sometimes was, and Grandma wasn't in the kitchen cooking tea as she usually was. Old Station wasn't in his basket either.

Nick found Grandma in the back garden, taking the washing off the line. "Nice windy day. Wanted to leave the washing out as long as possible," she said from behind a sheet. "I'll get your tea in a minute, dear."

"Where's Old Station?" Nick said. "He's not in his basket."

Grandma didn't reply,…

Michael Morpurgo

Classworks Fiction and Poetry Texts Year 3 © Eileen Jones, Nelson Thornes Ltd 2004

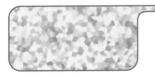

Teaching notes and ideas

Narrative: Setting

Stories with familiar settings

1 Barmkins are Best

Which word in the first few lines is particularly useful when starting a story? (Once.) Talk about how setting is put into place, before the action of the story starts. What does this setting involve? (People and place.) Ask the children to identify words and phrases that they think give the most effective descriptions. Why? **T1, T8**

Which phrase tells the reader that the action is beginning? (One day... .) Begin a class list of starter phrases, words or sentences. Ask the children to use books they are currently reading in order to add to the list. **T11**

2 Harry Potter and the Philosopher's Stone

Compare this opening with the previous one. Stress the picture of an ordinary place, ordinary people, ordinary day. Discuss the level of detail. (Greater emphasis on character than place.) Which words are particularly effective? Why? **T1, T8**

Point out the author's sentence telling the reader "our story starts".

Stress the writer's use of paragraphs – when and why they are begun.

Ask the children to write a similar story opening, of two or three paragraphs, set in a place they know well: their street, school or sports centre. **T15**

3 The Sunday Visit – Part One

The opening paragraphs answer the questions 'When?', 'Where?' and 'Who?' with particular emphasis on 'When?' **T1**

Which phrase tells the reader that the action is beginning? (One such Sunday.) Investigate the division into sentences and paragraphs. Try changing longer sentences into two short ones. **S10, S11**

Ask the children to identify words they do not know. Can they use context to guess the meanings? Confirm with dictionaries. **S1**

4 The Sunday Visit – Part Two

Point out the layout of the dialogue. Model write further conversation. **T15**

Reinforce knowledge of question marks; identify examples in the text. Convert statements in the story into questions. **S6**

Point out the 'tidy' way the story is ended, identifying helpful phrases and devices (the link with the title). Ask the children to write a new ending. **T11**

Speaking and listening

Discuss the different story settings. Which do the children prefer? Which makes the most effective background to the action of the story?

Encourage opinions with the use of supporting evidence.

Narrative: Dialogue

Stories with familiar settings

5 Pippi Starts School

Focus on dialogue and the way it is presented: the use of statements, questions, exclamations. Talk about paragraphs. Compare the number with those in *Harry Potter* (Text 2). Consider how paragraphs organise the structure of both story and dialogue. **T2**

Stress some of the punctuation and grammar rules of dialogue. Model write a continuation of the conversation between Pippi and the teacher. **S2, T10**

6 A Technical Problem

Reinforce teaching on the layout of dialogue. Emphasise the use of commas, and the common occurrence of exclamation marks. Point out the change into the present tense in dialogue sentences; contrast this with the past tense in the narrative paragraphs. Revise the past tense of some irregular verbs. **T2, S4, S7**

Ask the children to add dialogue, beginning new paragraphs as appropriate. **T15**

7 A Practical Solution

Investigate the different voices used here: the author (the storyteller); the narrator; the chorus. **T3**

Ask the children to list useful words for introducing and concluding dialogue ('said', 'replied', etc). **W19**

8 Fantastic Mr Fox

What do the children notice about the length of different paragraphs? Why are some so short? Why does the writer not always need to say who is speaking? **T2**

Review grammar, punctuation and rules of direct speech. Debate oral suggestions for Badger and Fox's conversation on their way home; transcribe into a written form. **S2**

Hold a word association oral session on a topic for a story. Record words, phrases and ideas. Help the children to plan a story which is organised in paragraphs and uses dialogue. Allow time for writing the story. **T15**

Speaking and listening

Share some of the children's own stories.

Let the children collaborate in presenting a story. Do the voices differentiate between speakers?

Plays

Oral and written plays

9–10 Fantastic Mr Fox

Compare this with the prose version (Text 8). Ask the children to identify differences. Work together, compiling a checklist of the key differences between prose and playscripts. Stress layout; the absence of speech marks; and the use of stage directions in italics. **T4**

Put the children into small groups to practise reading the playscript. **T4**

11 Making News

This is an extension to the script in *A Practical Solution* (Text 7). Use it as a starting point; ask the children to finish it, perhaps working in groups. **T14**

12–13 Fantastic Mr Fox

Prepare and read this final scene. Stress the benefit of the stage directions. **T4, T5**

Focus on verbs. Ask the children to identify the most expressive verbs. Make a list of the verbs describing movement ('glide', 'scarper', etc). **S3**

Return to a story already read. Make oral preparations, and then let the children write simple playscripts based on the story. **T14**

Speaking and listening

Share some group performances of *Fantastic Mr Fox* (Text 10).

Compare ideas for the end of *Making News*.

Rehearse and present a play.

Poetry

Poems based on observation and the senses

14 November Night

Point out the absence of rhyme. Consider the impact of particular words and their appeal to the senses. Identify words linked to sight and hearing. Are imaginative comparisons made?

Consider how layout is important, with shape reflecting meaning. Have the children noticed that the poem needs to be read from the bottom up? Can they work out 'punctured piping'? **T6**

Collaborate on a shape poem (on a subject with strong visual or auditory impact). **T13**

15 City Lights

Compare with the previous poem. Provide a list of starter prompts: rhyme; language; memorable words. **T8**

Which lights are mentioned? What are they compared to? Which descriptions are most effective? Which senses are involved? (For example, 'purring' involves hearing.) **T6**

16 The Mouse's Tale

Are there similarities to *November Night?* (A focus on shape.) Do the children spot the play on 'tail'? Ask the children to identify an important difference here from the last two poems (the use of rhyme). Why is rhyme not obvious immediately? (It is not always at end of line.) **T7**

Put the children into small groups to practise reciting the poem aloud. **T6**

Work as a class, writing a different animal's tale in an appropriate shape. **T13**

17 Wonder Birds

Point out the continued theme of animals. How are animals treated differently here? (This is a serious, observational poem.) Study the layout. Why is the final 'verse' set out in this way? Make sure the children identify relevant words in the other verses. **T6**

Collect words and phrases linked to a different bird or animal. Ask the children to create wordsearch patterns with some of them. **T13**

18 The Owl

Point out the continued thematic link. Ask the children for initial comments. Guide towards awareness of rhyme; repeated lines; careful selection of words. Which words are most effective? Do they appeal to the reader's senses?

Collect and display other effective words and phrases about an owl. Put the children into pairs to write a further verse for this poem. **T9, T13**

Speaking and listening

Listen to the group performances of *The Mouse's Tale*. **T6**

Exchange views on the poems, expressing preferences. Encourage the children to offer supporting evidence from the texts. **T8**

TERM 2

Narrative: Themes

Myths, legends and parables with related themes

19 A Pigeon and a Picture

Do the children recognise the genre? Identify features of a fable: clever or amusing short story; animal characters; a moral.

Ask the children to sequence events, using a storyboard format. **T7**

20 A Baboon and a Fox

Discuss the theme of this fable (clever over foolish). Consider other common story themes. Ask the children to plan their own fables using one of these themes. **T2, T9**

21 Osiris

Debate the genre (a myth). Identify key characteristics: gods; danger and violence; revenge; heroic character; ancient times.

What is the central theme of this story? (Good over evil.) Ask the children to sequence events using an appropriate format.

Use the story as the starting point for research on Egyptian mythology.

Focus on adjectives. Work on identifying and classifying adjectives. Which nouns do they qualify? How important are the adjectives? Add some of them to the children's new spelling lists. **S2, S3, W7**

22 The New Year Animals

Discuss the theme of the story (clever over strong). Can the children think of other stories with the same theme? **T2**

Identify any adjectives in the text describing the rat. What others would suit him? Talk about character portraits. Model write an example (of yourself, perhaps). Work on a character portrait of the rat. Brainstorm possible forms of presentation (missing person poster; newspaper article; letter between two of the other animals). **T8**

23 The Legend of King Canute

Talk about the theme (the importance of wisdom; recognition of the limits of human powers). Ask the children to identify features of a legend (heroic deeds; battles; often an element of truth). Which parts of the text are probably true? (People; places.) Which are probably not true? (Actually sitting on beach giving orders to the sea.)

Ask the children to explore the text for information about Canute's character. Then write a character portrait using an interesting format (for example, a poster). **T3, T8**

Speaking and listening

Discuss some of the story themes you have found in this unit.

Focus on particular characters, and investigate behaviour through role-play (child takes a part, and answers questions in character).

Listen to explanations of one another's sequencing work.

Narrative: Plot

Traditional stories

24 Anancy and Common Sense

Which words are a traditional opening? (Once upon a time... .) Which words in the story help to introduce an ending? (And so... .) Provide access to other books so that the children can make a collection of useful story openings and endings. **T1**

25 The Crocodile's Blessing – story opening

Compare the opening words to those in the previous story. Are you reminded of another traditional story? (*Cinderella.*) Make comparisons between characters, theme and setting in *Cinderella* (and *Alex and the Glass Slipper* and *Cinderboy* in *Classworks Literacy, Year 3*).

Ask the children to plan, by mapping or storyboard, the rest of this story. **T1, T7, T9**

26 The Crocodile's Blessing – story ending

Compare this with the ending of *Cinderella*. Identify traditional story language. Compare the ending with the children's plans.

27 The Lead

Discuss the theme of this modern story. Identify similarities with elements of the Cinderella stories.

Ask the children to plan their own traditional tale, using a known theme, but new, modern characters and setting. Discuss the best ways to plan. **T7, T9**

Allocate time for writing the stories.

Speaking and listening

Compare planning. Ask the children to talk about preferred methods.

Share some of the new stories.

Poetry

Poetry from different cultures

28 One Pink Sari

Which culture is being celebrated? Which words point to this?

Experiment with performance, identifying the need for volume to increase with the growing numbers. **T4**

Model write a second verse – using the same format of numbers – set in a different country. Then let the children work on writing new verses of their own. **T11**

29 Mother Parrot's Advice to her Children

Use atlases to identify the poem's place of origin. Discuss the meaning of the poem. Is the advice really just to parrots? (Perhaps from parents to children?)

Ask groups to prepare and rehearse performances of particular verses. **T4**, **T5**

Ask the children to add verses of their own. **T11**

30 Friendship

Discuss the message of the poem and its global application (it would make a good choice for use in a Class Assembly). Experiment with different readings: single or group voice; volume; tone; expression. Which words do the children find memorable? **T4**

Point out the absence of rhyme. Is there a particular pattern to the poem? Is repetition used?

Use this as a model for the children's own poems on friendship. **T11**

31 King Canute

Point out that culture involves not only place, but also time. Talk about the time period involved (eleventh century) and refer back to Text 23.

Identify unfamiliar words. Discuss deciphering strategies, pointing out the importance of an awareness of grammar (for example, 'panache' must be a noun). Encourage careful 'guessing', followed by dictionary confirmation. **S1**

Ask the children to plan a class performance; then pool ideas. **T4**

32–33 The Wind in a Frolic

Research the time period (nineteenth century). What evidence is there of a different culture? (Language; dress; customs.) Identify some unfamiliar words. Encourage the children to use effective strategies to decipher meaning. **S1**

Investigate the rhythm. Identify where the number of voices should be varied. Would background sounds be effective? (Musical instruments; voice.) **T4**

Put the children into groups to prepare and rehearse a performance of separate parts of the poem. **T5**

Speaking and listening

Rehearse and perform a class performance of *The Wind in a Frolic*.

Discuss which poem to use for a performance to other classes.

Begin rehearsals.

TERM 3

Narrative: Plot

Adventure and mystery stories

34 No Peace for Tom: Chapter One

Investigate setting. Does it focus mainly on 'Who?', 'When?' or 'Where?' ('Who?') Analyse the build up of plot, as problems and Tom's suspicions grow. Discuss the ending. **T2**, **T11**

Consider the use of paragraphs. Point out the link with dialogue. Practise using speech marks in new sentences. **S4**

35 No Peace for Tom: Chapter Two

How does the author develop her story? (New events; more problems.) **T1**, **T2**

Give the children more practice in using speech marks, putting the paragraph beginning 'Joe and Tom...' into dialogue form, with both boys speaking. **S4**

36 No Peace for Tom: Chapter Three

Has the plot developed? (New characters; potential twist of fortune.)

Focus on adjectives. Ask the children to identify them, the nouns they describe, and the effect they have. **T2**

Debate ideas for the children's own mystery and adventure stories.

37 No Peace for Tom: Chapter Four

Investigate how the solution to the predicament is now being put into place. Which words add to the atmosphere in this chapter? **T11**

Investigate the writer's use of conjunctions. Ask the children to identify the ways in which sentences have been joined. **S5**

38 No Peace for Tom: Chapter Five

Point out that here the writer must answer all the questions she has set. Why does Tom receive the final mention? (He is the hero – compare the opening to Chapter One and the title of the story.)

Ask the children to list the main points of the story in sequence. **T1**

Begin work on the children's own stories, using this sequence of chapters as a model. Emphasise the need for good planning, before writing the stories. **T10, T11**

Speaking and listening

What genre is this? (adventure/mystery). Which parts of the story worked best? Identify effective words the writer used.

Share the role of storyteller, re-telling the story of *No Peace for Tom*.

Narrative: Perspective/character

Range of stories

39 The Holiday

Who is the main character? (I.) Explain the difference between first and third person accounts. Discuss possible advantages ('getting inside' the character's mind), and disadvantages (not knowing immediately who 'I' is). **T3**

Discuss feelings. Do the storyteller's feelings seem true to life? Encourage references to the text. Explain that the writer has **based it** on memories of his childhood. It is a mixture of fact and fiction. Which parts are probably fact? (Names of people and places.) Which parts are probably fiction? (Actual words of conversation.) **T4, T5**
Ask the children to identify pronouns in the extract. Explain their use and function. Distinguish pronoun types, with particular focus on personal pronouns. **S2**

40 The Marble Crusher

Revise first and third person accounts. Can the children label this text? Which words offer clues? (Pronouns.) **T3**

Discuss Albert's feelings and how they change. Ask the children to identify important words or clues (for example, 'twiddle his hair' – indicating nervousness). Ask the children about the teacher's words and reaction: was he behaving reasonably? **T5**

Ask the children to write a first person account of the incident, taking one of the roles. Emphasise the need to reveal in their words how they feel, and what they think about the other character. **T12**

41 Bill's New Frock

Focus on the way in which Bill is treated. Are the footballers behaving reasonably? Are they being fair in attitudes and use of the playground? Discuss how Bill feels, and how characters could have behaved differently.

Ask the children to write a first person account of a playtime incident. **T12**

42 A Little Princess

Discuss the behaviour of Miss Minchin. Is she fair to Sara? Why is she annoyed? Can the children empathise with Sara?

Ask the children to list words which offer clues to the character's feelings. **T5**

Speaking and listening

Debate the credibility of Bill's playground experiences in *Bill's New Frock*. Widen the discussion to personal experiences. Could the children's playtimes and playground be improved?

Ask the children to put themselves in Sara's place (Text 42). Encourage them to describe their feelings.

Poetry

Range of poems including humour

43–44 Jim who ran away from his nurse, and was eaten by a lion

Talk about the poetic classification. What does 'cautionary' mean? Do the children know other examples of cautionary poems?

Discuss the rhyming pattern (couplets). Establish the rhythm by clapping or counting syllables. **T15**

Stress the value of hearing the poem. Organise group preparations and rehearsals of the poem to present it to another group. **T7**

45 Bawling Bertie

Ask the children to make comparisons with the last poem, identifying similarities and differences.

Focus on language: alliteration, onomatopoeia, word play (the idiom, 'getting on someone's goat'; the link between 'goat' and 'kid'). **T6**, **T7**

Use the poem as a model for the children's own writing, with an emphasis on alliterative and onomatopoeic words. **T15**

Use ICT to create final, published forms. Stress the impact on the audience of font and layout. **T21**

46 *From* The Dong with a Luminous Nose

Why does the poem seem 'nonsense'? (Many words seem to be made up.) Set the task of identifying words which emphasise sound. Which words do the children think are effective? Why?

Ask the children to plot the rhyme scheme. Is there a regular pattern? **T7**

Work on spelling patterns, revising letter strings such as *-ight*.

Provide resources for the children to select other enjoyable poems to include in this humorous category. Ask them to be prepared to justify their choices. **T6**

Speaking and listening

Listen to the group readings of *Jim...* (Texts 43–44).

Hold a poetry reading session, listening to one another's recitations of:

- the children's own poems
- new selections, justifying their choices.

Authors

Stories by the same author

47 Mortimer's Cross

Does anyone know this story? Identify it as one of a series of books featuring the same characters. Debate advantages and disadvantages of a series for an author and reader. Compare reactions to this text. **T9**

Focus on sentence construction, investigating Aiken's use of conjunctions. **S5**

48 The Mystery of Mr Jones's Disappearing Taxi

How does this story compare with the last one? Is it better, more interesting or funnier? What do the two stories have in common? Do you like this author? Encourage the children to offer opinions and to justify preferences. **T1**, **T8**, **T9**

Discuss and model formats for book reviews. **T14**

49 The Angel of Nitshill Road

Compare this with *Bill's New Frock* (Text 41). Explore similarities: school life; an element of fantasy; comical situations. Which extract do the children prefer? Encourage textual reference. Do the children know more of Fine's work. Use a website – for example, *www.channel4.com/learning/microsites/B/bookbox* – to find out more about the author. **T8**, **T9**

Ask the children to list in order the 'proof' of Celeste's difference. **T1**

50 Conker

Relate this to other texts by Morpurgo (Text 40 or *Classworks Literacy Year 3* page 20). Ask the children for their views on this author, and how one story compares with another. Talk about themes that he has used. Do his books have common features? (Animals; children on their own; awareness of emotions.)

Provide Internet access for an interview with Morpurgo, for example: *www.mystworld.com/youngwriter/authors/authors.html*

Ask the children to write a book review for their own age group. Make the review about a book they have read this year.

Speaking and listening

Share some of the children's book reviews.

Hold a discussion on authors, expressing preferences and referring to examples. Would a local writer come in to talk to the children?